# Cast list

Miss Jackson

Martin

Katie

Alice

Joe/Miller

Marge/Miller's wife

## Scene 1

*Outside an old house in the country. **Katie**, **Martin**, and **Alice** enter, carrying backpacks. Their teacher, **Miss Jackson**, enters behind them.*

**Miss Jackson**   Here we are, children. This is the house where we'll be staying.

**Martin**   Wow! It's so big!

**Alice**   And so old!

**Katie**   And so... spooky!

**Martin**   Yes! I bet it's haunted.

**Miss Jackson**    That's enough of that, Martin. Of course it isn't haunted –

*Joe enters behind them.*

**Joe**    Can I help you?

*His voice makes them jump with surprise. They all turn to him.*

**Miss Jackson**    Oh! Hello... I'm Miss Jackson. From the school. I've brought some children here for a weekend course.

**Joe**    Oh, yes. Are they all here?

| Miss Jackson | No. The rest are on the bus. They'll be here in a minute. |

*She speaks to the children.*

| | Why don't you go and get yourselves settled, while I see to the others? |
| Alice | All right, Miss Jackson. |
| Miss Jackson | Good. I'll see you in a moment. |

*Miss Jackson goes. Joe speaks to the children.*

| Joe | In you come, then. This way. |

*Joe leads them through into the house. As they go through, the* **children** *narrate.*

**Alice**          The man leads us through into the house.

**Martin**      It's old and it's dark.

**Katie**         It's dim and it's gloomy.

**Alice**          We look around at the wooden walls.

**Martin**      The cobwebs on the ceiling, the rickety staircase.

| Katie | And we wonder if we're going to like it here at all. |
|---|---|

*Joe speaks to the children.*

| Joe | Here we are. Put your bags down there for a moment. |
|---|---|

*The **children** put their bags down. They speak to each other.*

| Alice | I thought this was supposed to be a youth hostel? |
|---|---|

| Martin | I know. It looks more like a museum. |
|---|---|

| Katie | And it's cold. Why is it so cold? |
|---|---|

| Joe | It's always cold here. Always cold and chilly, even in the summer. |
|---|---|

| Katie | Why? |
|---|---|

| Joe | Because of the – |
|---|---|

*Marge has entered. She interrupts Joe before he finishes his sentence.*

| Marge | Joe! That's enough of that! You're not trying to scare the children before they've settled in, are you? |
|---|---|

*She comes forward to the children, speaking to them.*

**Marge**        Hello. My name's Marge. And this is Joe. You mustn't mind him. He likes to have his little joke, don't you, Joe?

**Joe**        Yes.

**Marge**    We run the youth hostel together.

**Martin**    It's very old, isn't it?

**Marge**    Oh, yes. It's five hundred years old. It used to be a mill.

**Katie**    Is that why there's a water-wheel in the stream outside?

**Marge**    Yes. That was part of the mill. They used to store malt here. But that was a long time ago.

**Joe**    And in those days –

**Marge**    *(To Joe)* Why don't you go out and help their teacher bring the rest of the children in, Joe. I'll show these up to their rooms.

> *Joe goes. **Marge** speaks to the children.*

Get your things and follow me up the stairs. And don't worry. They might be a bit rickety, but they're quite safe!

## Scene 2

*The **children** and **Marge** stay on stage. The **children** narrate their journey up the stairs to the audience, while **Marge** remains still, with her back to the children.*

**Alice**      We climb the stairs.

**Martin**      They twist and turn.

**Katie**      They creak underfoot.

**Alice**      And halfway up –

**Martin**      Where the stairs turn to the right –

**Katie**      She stops, and she turns to us, and she says –

*Marge turns to the children.*

**Marge**      You are now looking at one of the oldest things in the house.

**Martin**      You don't mean you, do you?

**Katie**      Martin! Don't be cheeky!

**Martin**      Sorry. It was only a joke.

| | |
|---|---|
| **Marge** | (*Smiling*) That's all right. And, no, I don't mean me. I mean this. This tapestry here on the wall. Do you know what a tapestry is? |
| **Alice** | I do! It's a picture that's been sewn. |
| **Marge** | That's right. Or woven. |
| **Alice** | My gran makes them. But they're not as big as this one. |
| **Marge** | This tapestry here is as old as the house. |
| **Katie** | Five hundred years! |
| **Marge** | Yes. And it shows life as it used to be lived here. You can look at it, but you mustn't touch it. It's so old it might crumble. |

*The **children** look at the tapestry, and describe what they see.*

| | |
|---|---|
| **Alice** | We gather and look at the large tapestry on the wall... |
| **Martin** | ...So old its colours have faded with age. |
| **Katie** | We look at the pictures there, and this is what we see. |
| **Alice** | In the centre's the mill, as it was then. |
| **Martin** | In front of the mill, a red-faced man on a donkey. |
| **Katie** | A thin woman running after him. |
| **Alice** | Her bony hand stretching out towards him. |
| **Martin** | But he's not bothered about her. |
| **Katie** | He just sits there on his donkey, laughing. |
| **Alice** | And men are working in the fields. |
| **Martin** | And a piper's piping, and people are dancing. |
| **Katie** | And there they all are, frozen in time. |

| Alice | Forever dancing. |
|---|---|
| Martin | Forever singing. |
| Katie | And the woman forever calling to the man on the donkey. |

*The **children** turn and speak to Marge.*

| Alice | Who are all these people? |
|---|---|
| Martin | Who's that man on the donkey? |
| Marge | That's the miller. He's holding a jar of ale in his hands. We call it beer nowadays. He made ale with the malt from his mill. |
| Martin | It looks to me as if he liked to drink it as well. |
| Marge | Yes. I'm afraid he did. He loved his ale – but he didn't love his wife. |
| Katie | Is that the thin lady who looks so sad? |
| Marge | Yes. And she had a very good reason to be sad, as well. I'll tell you her story – |

***Katie** suddenly interrupts her.*

| | |
|---|---|
| **Katie** | What's that smell? I suddenly smelled something, just then! *(She speaks to Alice and Martin)* Can you smell it? |
| **Alice** | I can smell something... |
| **Martin** | It's just the damp – |
| **Katie** | No, it isn't. It's not the damp... it's something else... a kind of sweet smell... |

16

| | |
|---|---|
| **Marge** | It's the smell of malt. |
| **Alice** | Malt? Isn't that what the miller used to make ale with? |
| **Marge** | Yes. |
| **Alice** | But you don't make it now? |
| **Marge** | It hasn't been made for a long time. |
| **Martin** | Then how can we smell it? |
| **Marge** | People say they do smell it from time to time. It comes and it goes. One minute it's there and the next – |
| **Katie** | It's gone! |
| **Marge** | That's right. |
| **Katie** | It has gone! Just as suddenly as it came. |
| **Marge** | And I can hear that the rest of your class has arrived. What a noise! It's enough to frighten anybody off! I'll go and greet them. Your rooms are just at the top of the stairs. |
| **Martin** | What about the story you were going to tell us? |

| Marge | That will have to wait till later, now. |
|---|---|

*Marge goes.*

| Alice | I wonder what that story is? |
|---|---|
| Martin | Maybe it's a ghost story! Maybe there's a ghost in the house! And maybe that smell was a ghost smell! |
| Katie | Shut up, Martin! |
| Martin | I know a ghost story. There was this ghost, and he kept bumping into things. You know why? Because he needed spooktacles! |

*Martin laughs. Alice and Katie*
*roll their eyes at Martin's bad joke.*

**Alice**    Come on, Katie. Let's go and get settled in
before the others get here.

*Alice and Katie go. Martin runs*
*after them, trying to scare them.*

**Martin**    I'm a ghost, and I'm coming to get you! Woooo!

*He goes.*

## Scene 3

*It's later that evening, in a large room in the old house.* **Miss Jackson** *enters. She speaks to the audience, as if they are the rest of the children.*

**Miss Jackson**   Is everyone settled into their rooms, now? Good. And did you all enjoy your tea? It was delicious, wasn't it? Especially after that long journey. You've all got your notebooks, haven't you? Well, now. Let me tell you why we've come up here. This is called Room One, and it's right at the –

> *Martin, Alice, and Katie enter.*
> *Martin is telling a joke.*

**Martin**      What's a ghost's favourite meal?

**Alice**       I don't know.

**Martin**      Spooketti!

> *He laughs. The others don't, but*
> *Miss Jackson smiles a little, then*
> *tries to be stern.*

**Miss Jackson**    You're late, children.

**Katie**       Sorry, Miss Jackson. It's Martin. He keeps telling us terrible jokes about ghosts.

**Martin**      What does a ghost have for breakfast? Hot buttered ghost and dreaded wheat!

**Miss Jackson**    Thank you, Martin. *(To the three of them)* Here are your notebooks and pencils. Sit down with the others.

*She gives them a notebook and pencil each. They go and sit down. **Miss Jackson** carries on speaking to everyone.*

**Miss Jackson**  As I was saying, this is Room One, and it's at the very top of the house –

**Martin**  What's a ghost's favourite pudding? I scream!

**Miss Jackson**  *(Warning)* That's enough, Martin.

**Martin**  It'll have to be, Miss Jackson. I don't know any more jokes.

**Alice**  Thank goodness for that!

**Miss Jackson**     As you know, we've come here on a story and poem writing weekend. While you're here, I want you to write down everything you see and hear, all that you think, and feel, and find out. And the first thing you're going to find out about is the history of this house.

**Alice**     Marge started to tell us a story about the miller and his wife. Do you know that story, Miss Jackson?

**Miss Jackson**     Yes, I do. And that story happened right here, in this room.

**Katie**     Will you tell us?

**Miss Jackson**     That's just what I'm going to do. Gather round and listen.

*She sits. The three **children** gather round her. She begins to tell the story.*

This house is full of history.

This house is full of mystery.

The house is full of stories, and here is just one of them...

*Alice, **Martin**, and **Katie** narrate.*

**Alice**        We sit in the room. No one makes a sound.

**Martin**       It's dark outside, and the wind's blowing.

**Katie**        And we listen as Miss Jackson starts to tell us the story.

**Miss Jackson**  It was long, long ago in this very room. This is where the sacks of malt were stored. There used to be planks between those beams above your heads. And those beams – well, they could tell a story –

**Alice**        But she doesn't get any further!

| | |
|---|---|
| **Martin** | Because suddenly outside a storm breaks! |
| **Katie** | And the rain lashes down! |
| **Alice** | And lightning flashes! |
| **Martin** | And thunder booms! |
| **Katie** | And the wind rattles and howls at the window! |

> *Katie*, **Alice**, *and* **Martin** *all cry out together.*

| | |
|---|---|
| **Katie**<br>**Alice**<br>**Martin** } | Aaaaaaaaaaa! |

> *Miss Jackson jumps up.*

| | |
|---|---|
| **Miss Jackson** | There's no need to be scared! It's only a storm. Quick, everyone! Get your notebooks and pencils! Write down everything you see and hear and feel about the storm! |
| **Alice** | But what about the story, Miss Jackson? |
| **Miss Jackson** | I'll tell you that another time. The storm's here, now, and it won't last long. Get writing! |

**Martin**     So we look out of the window at the rain and
the lightning.

**Katie**      And we write down our thoughts – and these
are mine.

*Katie reads from her book.*

**Katie**

The beast is outside
blowing and roaring.
Or is it the wind and the thunder?

The beast is outside
crying and whimpering.
Or is it the trickling rain?
Yes, the beast is outside
wailing and howling.
Or is it the wind through the trees?

Oh, the beast is outside
he is slinking away
like a cat
that has caught his prey.

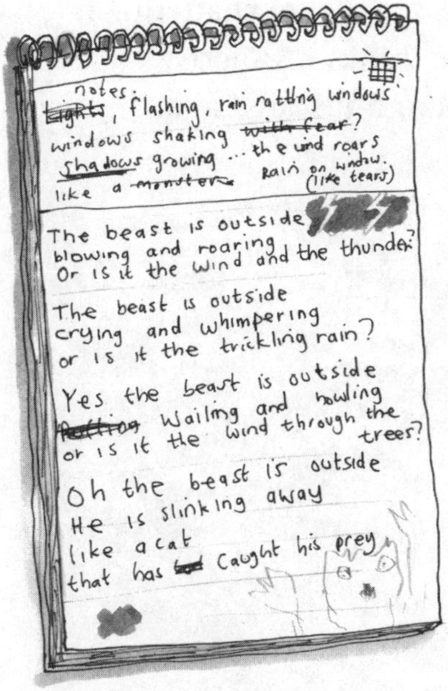

| | |
|---|---|
| **Alice** | That's really good, that is, Katie. |
| **Katie** | Thanks. |
| **Martin** | Mine's good as well. Do you want to hear it? |
| **Alice** | Go on, then. |

*Martin reads.*

| | |
|---|---|
| **Martin** | Flashes of lightning |
| | Katie thinks they're frightening |
| | Katie thinks it's spooky |
| | But I'm not scared at all |
| | |
| | The windows are rattling |
| | Katie's teeth are chattering |
| | Katie thinks it's spooky |
| | But I'm not scared at all |

I'm not afraid of stuff like that
I'm not a scaredy cat
Kate thinks it's spooky
But I'm not scared at all.

**Alice**        What a stupid poem!

**Martin**       It's not! It's good, isn't it, Miss Jackson?

**Miss Jackson**  Yes, very good, Martin, but I'm sure there are a few things that scare you too.

**Martin**       I'm not scared of *anything*, Miss.

**Miss Jackson**  Well, I'm afraid that will have to wait for another day. It's time for bed now, Martin.

**Martin**       Oh, Miss –

**Miss Jackson**  And everyone else. Come on, all of you, it's late. Make sure you all pick up your books and pencils. Right? Good. Off we go.

> ***Miss Jackson**, **Martin**, and **Alice** go. **Katie** remains alone. She sits, fed up.*

## Scene 4

*Katie, still alone on stage, speaks to the audience.*

**Katie**     Martin's right, though. I *am* scared. Scared of everything in this big old house. Even my own poem scares me. And later on, when I'm in my room and the lights are out, it gets even worse.

*She settles down to sleep.*

I can't get that tapestry out of my mind. I can't get the sweet smell of malt out of my mind. I lie in my bed in the dark, and even though the storm has stopped, I still hear noises.

*The actors who play **Alice**, **Martin**, **Miss Jackson**, and **Joe** now enter and speak as narrators, describing the sounds that Katie hears. Their voices are scary, and **Katie** reacts, scared, to them.*

| | |
|---|---|
| **Alice** | Traffic whooshing in the rain outside. |
| **Martin** | Scratching noises from the roof above. |
| **Miss Jackson** | Gurglings and snufflings – |
| **Joe** | Creakings and shufflings – |

*Katie speaks aloud to herself.*

| | |
|---|---|
| **Katie** | It's just the water-pipes! It's just owls in the loft! There's nothing to be scared of, nothing at all! |
| **Alice** | Oh, yes, there is, there's a lot to be scared of – |
| **Martin** | A lot to be scared of in an old house at night. |
| **Miss Jackson** | Those two red eyes shining in through the window – |

**Joe**              They're the red, staring eyes of a terrible beast!

**Katie**            No, they're not! It's just the light from the lamp-
                     post outside.

**Alice**            Or is it a monster –

**Martin**           A monster –

**Miss Jackson**     A monster?

**Joe**              Are they the red, staring eyes of a monster?

**Katie**            No! There is no such thing as a monster. There
                     is no such thing as a monster!

**Alice**            Now it's late at night and everyone's asleep.

**Martin**　　　And only Katie's still wide awake.

**Miss Jackson**　　And she hears the stairs on the landing creak.

**Joe**　　　And she hears the padding of soft feet.

**Alice**　　Closer and closer.

**Martin**　　The door opens.

**Miss Jackson**    Closer and closer.

**Joe**    Someone comes into the room.

**Alice**    Closer and closer.

**Martin**    A thin woman.

**Miss Jackson**    Closer and closer.

**Joe**    With a bony hand.

*All four speak together.*

**All**          Closer and closer and closer and closer!

***Katie*** *cries out in fear.*

**Katie**       It's the tapestry! It's come to life! The tapestry's alive and it's coming to get me!

*Marge enters and speaks to Katie.*
*The other four actors go.*

**Marge**     Are you not asleep yet, dear?

*Katie sees Marge.*

**Katie**     Marge! It's you!

**Marge**     Who did you think it might be?

**Katie**     I... don't know...

**Marge**     I was just checking on everyone. One or two of
the children in the other rooms have had a little
trouble settling. So we've made a hot milky
drink. Would you like to come down and have
some?

**Katie**     Yes, please, Marge!
That would be lovely!

**Marge**     Come on, then.
We've got a fire
going as well.

**Katie**     It sounds wonderful. Thank you.

*Katie and Marge go.*

## Scene 5

*It's the next morning.* **Miss Jackson** *enters and speaks again to the audience as if they are the children.*

**Miss Jackson**   Good morning, everyone. Did everyone sleep all right last night? I hope so. And I hope everyone's made their beds and tidied their rooms. In fact, while you're all here, I'll just go and check. And when I come back, I'll tell you that story.

*Miss Jackson* goes. *Katie, Alice, and Martin* enter. *Alice is speaking to Katie.*

**Alice**   And did they really give you a milky drink?

**Katie**   Yes. It was delicious. And it had that malty smell. Didn't it, Martin?

| | |
|---|---|
| **Martin** | That's because it was made from malt. |
| **Alice** | *(Surprised)* Were you there, Martin? |
| **Martin** | Yes – |
| **Alice** | So you were spooked as well! |
| **Martin** | No! I wasn't spooked. I just had a bit of trouble sleeping with all the traffic noise. *(He sounds a bit anxious)* That's right, isn't it, Katie? |
| **Katie** | Yes. That's right, Martin. |

*Miss Jackson enters.*

| | |
|---|---|
| **Miss Jackson** | All the beds seem to be nice and tidy – except one. |

*She looks hard at Martin.*

Martin?

| | |
|---|---|
| **Martin** | Sorry, Miss Jackson. |

*Miss Jackson sighs.*

| | |
|---|---|
| **Miss Jackson** | It's in such a state. You'll have to go and tidy it. |
| **Martin** | Yes, Miss Jackson. I'll do it later. |

*Joe* enters.

| | |
|---|---|
| **Joe** | Excuse me, Miss Jackson. We usually ask one of the children to help with the washing-up after meals. I wonder if young Martin here could come and give me a hand? |
| **Martin** | Er – |
| **Miss Jackson** | I'm sure he'd love to. Wouldn't you, Martin? |
| **Martin** | Yes, Miss Jackson. |
| **Miss Jackson** | And when you've done that, you can go and tidy your room. |
| **Martin** | Yes, Miss Jackson. |

| | |
|---|---|
| **Joe** | Come on, then, Martin. Looks like you've got a busy morning ahead of you. |

> *Joe and Martin go. Miss Jackson speaks to Katie.*

| | |
|---|---|
| **Miss Jackson** | I hear you and Martin had a bit of trouble sleeping last night. |
| **Katie** | I did... get a bit scared... |
| **Alice** | So did I... a bit... it was all those noises. |
| **Miss Jackson** | It is a very noisy old house. Everything creaks and squeaks. But that's just because it's old – not because it's spooky. |

| | |
|---|---|
| **Katie** | I thought I heard a monster. |
| **Miss Jackson** | There's no monster here. But some people say there is a ghost – |
| **Alice** | A ghost? |
| **Miss Jackson** | Don't worry, Alice. There are no such things as ghosts. But I'll tell you the story. |
| **Katie** | The one from yesterday? |
| **Miss Jackson** | That's right. |
| **Alice** | I wonder if it's the same one Marge was going to tell us. The one about the tapestry. |
| **Miss Jackson** | Yes. It is that story. Sit down, everyone, and I'll tell you. And you, Katie, can tell it to Martin later. |
| **Katie** | Yes, Miss Jackson. I just hope it doesn't scare him! |

*Katie* and *Alice* sit. *Miss Jackson* sits and tells the story.

| | |
|---|---|
| **Miss Jackson** | Right, then. Here it is. Once, long ago, a miller and his wife lived here. The miller was fond of drink, but he was not fond of hard work. |

*The person who plays **Joe** enters*
*as the **miller**, drinking from a jug.*

**Miller**       I love my ale! Why should I work? My wife can
do all the work and leave me to drink my ale!

*He drinks.*

**Miss Jackson**       His wife wasn't happy about this, of course. And
she made sure the miller knew how unhappy
she was.

*The person who plays **Marge***
*enters as the **miller's wife**.*

**Wife**       There's no end to this work! I never stop,
morning, noon and night! And what do you do
to help? Nothing!

42

**Miller**        Be quiet with your nagging, woman!

**Miss Jackson**  And so it went on, for years –

**Wife**          All you do is sit and drink your ale!

**Miller**        That's just as it should be!

**Miss Jackson**  And years –

**Wife**          What are you good for? Nothing!

**Miller**        Shut up, woman, and leave me in peace!

**Miss Jackson**  And years!

**Wife**          You're just a lazy, good-for-nothing drunkard!
                  And it's not fair or right!

*The **miller's wife** goes.*

**Miller**          That wife of mine! I'm tired of her nagging. I wish I could find a way to make her shut up.

**Miss Jackson**    And one day that good-for-nothing miller had an idea – an awful, terrible idea!

**Miller**          That's it! I know just what to do!

*The **miller** goes.*

**Miss Jackson**    He came up this room, Room One. It was the place where they used to store the malt. The floor in those days was just loose planks of wood laid down on the beams. He came up here and took one of those planks away. And when his wife brought a sack of malt up here, she put her foot down – on nothing! And she fell down to her death!

*Off stage, the **miller's wife**
screams. The **miller** enters.*

**Miller**  That's put an end to her nagging. Now I'll have
me a quiet life!

**Miss Jackson**  But he was wrong. From that day on he had no
peace, or quiet. Because his wife haunted him.

*The **miller's wife** enters. The
**miller** sees her.*

**Wife**  I'll haunt you all your days. I'll never let you
rest. You'll have no peace from me!

*The **miller** cries out.*

**Miller**  No! No! No!

*He runs off.*

**Miss Jackson**  He went mad. He left the mill. It looked as if the mill would go to ruin. But it didn't. Because as soon as he'd gone, the mill started to shine.

**Wife**  Now the place is mine. I'll always keep it tidy and clean. And there'll always be a welcome for whoever comes here.

*She goes.*

| | |
|---|---|
| **Miss Jackson** | People say it's the ghost of the miller's wife still looking after the place. She's happy in her work now the miller has gone. But of course, it's just a story. No one really believes in ghosts – |

*Martin enters.*

| | |
|---|---|
| **Martin** | All right! Who's the joker? |
| **Miss Jackson** | Martin – ! |
| **Martin** | Who's been in my room and tidied all the stuff away? |
| **Miss Jackson** | What's that? |
| **Martin** | I went to tidy my room, like you said, and somebody had already done it! |
| **Alice** | It must have been the miller's wife. |
| **Miss Jackson** | You know better than that, Alice. It was probably Joe – |

**Martin** It couldn't have been him. We were washing up together. *(To Alice)* Who's the miller's wife?

| | |
|---|---|
| **Alice** | *(Excited)* Miss Jackson's just told us all about her. She's a ghost who wanders about the mill, tidying up – |
| **Miss Jackson** | *(Firmly)* It was Marge, then. Not a ghost. There are no such things as ghosts. *(She speaks to everyone)* Right, everyone. Off to your rooms and see what you can write about the story. And while you're doing that, I want to have a look at just how tidy Martin's room is. |

> **Miss Jackson** *and* **Alice** *go.*

| | |
|---|---|
| **Katie** | Martin – I'm not sure it *was* Marge who tidied your room. |
| **Martin** | Neither am I. My things weren't just tidied away – they were polished! And I saw Marge outside hanging out some washing. And there was that funny smell in the air – |
| **Katie** | Malt! |

| | |
|---|---|
| **Martin** | That's right. |
| **Katie** | You think it was the ghost, then? |
| **Martin** | I don't know. But there's one way to find out. We can do a bit of ghost-hunting. |
| **Katie** | How? |
| **Martin** | The first thing we've got to do, is make the ghost come to one of our rooms. |
| **Katie** | We could leave a terrible mess – that would attract her. |
| **Martin** | Right. And we could tie string between all the things – |
| **Katie** | And tie the string to some bells and piles of books – |
| **Martin** | There are some old sheep-bells in one of the rooms downstairs! |
| **Katie** | And then if the ghost moves the things, the bells will ring – |
| **Martin** | And the books will fall over – |

**Katie**      And we can run in –

**Martin**     And I'll take her picture with my camera!

**Katie**      Great! A ghost-trap!

**Martin**     We'll set it tonight, after everyone's gone to bed.

*He starts to go.*

**Katie**      Martin. Do you really think we should?

**Martin**     Katie. I really think we should.

**Katie**      Right, then. We will!

***Martin** goes.*

*Scene 6*                           ***Katie*** *speaks to the audience.*

**Katie**          So we do. We set the trap, just like we planned.
And then we go to bed. And there's something
very strange. The night before, I couldn't get to
sleep at all, I was so scared. But tonight, I want
to stay awake and I can't, and I'm not scared at
all.

***Kate*** *settles down to sleep.*

I can hear the pigeons cooing in the loft, and all
the other creakings and gurglings and
squeakings sound warm and friendly. So warm
and friendly and cosy, that soon I'm drifting off
to sleep.

Then, all of a sudden, there's a terrible crash!

*We hear a terrible crashing sound.*

And then an awful howling!

*Someone howls.*

And everyone's awake and running towards the noise!

> *Alice and Martin run on stage.*
> *Martin has a camera.*

Alice          What's that noise? It's coming from that room over there!

Martin        It's our ghost-trap! It's worked!

Alice          What?

Katie          Me and Martin have set a trap for the ghost!

Martin        And now I'm going to take a picture of her!

> *Martin goes to the side of the stage. The howling carries on.*

Alice          That doesn't sound much like a ghost to me, you know.

Katie          It doesn't, does it?

Alice          It sounds more like –

*Miss Jackson enters, facing Martin. Wrapped around her is a long piece of string with bells and books tied on it.*

| | |
|---|---|
| **Martin** | Miss Jackson! |
| **Miss Jackson** | What idiot did this! You, Martin! Was it you? |
| **Martin** | Yes... Miss Jackson... |
| **Katie** | And it was me, Miss Jackson. |

*Miss Jackson tries to walk but trips over the string and has to sit down.*

| | |
|---|---|
| **Miss Jackson** | What on *earth* did the two of you think you were doing? |
| **Katie** | I'm sorry, Miss Jackson – |
| **Miss Jackson** | Help me get out of this! |

> ***Katie**, **Martin**, and **Alice**
> untangle Miss Jackson.*

| | |
|---|---|
| | Well? What were you doing? |
| **Katie** | It was a ghost-trap, Miss Jackson. |
| **Martin** | To try and catch the ghost. |
| **Katie** | Martin was going to take a photograph of her. |

| | |
|---|---|
| **Martin** | With my camera. |
| **Miss Jackson** | Were you, now? Well, you didn't trap a ghost, did you? You trapped me! *(She rubs her ankle)* And I've bruised my ankle. |
| **Katie** | We're really sorry, Miss Jackson. |
| **Martin** | We didn't mean any harm. |
| **Katie** | I think we've just been... a bit silly... |

*Miss Jackson* is now untangled. She stands up. She is still very angry.

| | |
|---|---|
| **Miss Jackson** | More than a bit silly, Katie. How many times do I have to tell you? There is no such thing as a ghost! |
| **Alice** | *(To Martin)* Fancy believing in ghosts! I knew Katie did, but not you, Martin. |

*As **Alice** speaks, **Marge** enters
behind them, carrying a large
white shirt in front of her. Only
**Martin** can see her. He looks at
the shirt in fear.*

**Alice**          Look at you. You've gone all red. Your ears are
                   glowing! And your face! It looks like a beetroot!

**Martin**         Look! Behind you! Look!

**Alice**          Don't try that old trick. You won't scare us.

**Martin**         It's... not a trick... look...

**Miss Jackson**   What are you talking about now?

                   *** Miss Jackson** and **Alice** turn
                   round. They see the shirt and cry
                   out in fear.*

**Miss Jackson** } AAAAAAAH!
**Alice**

58

*Marge lowers the shirt, so they can see her face.*

**Marge**     Oh! Did I make you jump? Sorry. I was just getting in one of Joe's shirts from the line outside. I forgot it was out there, and he needs it for the morning.

**Alice**     We thought it was a ghost. Didn't we, Miss Jackson?

**Marge**     A ghost? Goodness me, how silly. Fancy being frightened by a shirt. Especially you, Miss Jackson.

**Miss Jackson**     I think the best thing we can do is forget all about ghosts. We all need some sleep. And we all need to remind ourselves... What do we need to remind ourselves?

*Alice, Martin, and Katie speak together.*

Alice  
Martin  } There is no such thing as a ghost!  
Katie

*Miss Jackson, Martin, Alice, and Katie go. Marge watches them, smiles to herself, then folds the shirt. Joe enters.*

Joe        What was all that noise about?

Marge        Some of the children set a trap for our ghost.

Joe        Did they, now?

Marge        But they trapped their teacher instead.

Joe        Well, well. Trying to trap our ghost. As if they could!

Marge        I know. Silly, isn't it?

*They go.*

## Scene 7

*The next day.* **Katie**, **Martin**, *and* **Alice** *enter, with* **Miss Jackson**. *She speaks to them.*

**Miss Jackson**  Here we are, then, everyone. Our last day. Hasn't the time passed quickly? I hope you've all enjoyed yourselves.

**Alice**  We have, Miss Jackson.

**Martin**  It's been great.

**Katie**  I'd love to come again.

| | |
|---|---|
| **Miss Jackson** | I'm glad. And I'm very pleased with all of you. You've tried lots of new activities. You've found out about the history of the area and this house, and I can see you've made lots of notes that we can use when we get back to school. And, Katie, I think you've learned something else. |
| **Katie** | Yes, Miss Jackson. There is no such thing as a ghost. |
| **Miss Jackson** | Good. Now, we have to pack and tidy up. And some of us have quite a lot to tidy up, haven't we, Martin? |
| **Martin** | Yes, Miss Jackson. |
| **Miss Jackson** | Right. Off you go, then. |
| | *The **children** turn and speak to the audience.* |
| **Alice** | So we go to our rooms to tidy up. |
| **Martin** | But when we get there, we have a surprise. |
| **Katie** | Because every piece of paper's been picked up. |
| **Miss Jackson** | Every pencil shaving has been swept away. |
| **Alice** | Every coat's been hung up. |

| | |
|---|---|
| **Martin** | Every bed made. |
| **Katie** | Everything's neat and tidy and clean. |

*Marge enters.*

| | |
|---|---|
| **Marge** | And – there's a smell of malt in the air. |

*The **children** and **Miss Jackson** all look at each other.*

*Joe enters.*

| | |
|---|---|
| **Joe** | But that's just me, making my milky, malted drink. |

*He drinks.*

| | |
|---|---|
| **Marge** | Or is it? |

*Joe and **Marge** look at each other and smile.*

# Treetops Playscripts
## Titles in the series include:

**Stage 10**
**The Masked Cleaning Ladies of Om**
by John Coldwell;
adapted by David Calcutt
  single: 0 19 918780 0
  pack of 6: 0 19 918781 9

**Stupid Trousers**
by Susan Gates;
adapted by David Calcutt
  single: 0 19 918782 7
  pack of 6: 0 19 918783 5

**Stage 11**
**Bertha's Secret Battle**
by John Coldwell;
adapted by David Calcutt
  single: 0 19 918786 X
  pack of 6: 0 19 918787 8

**Bertie Wiggins' Amazing Ears**
by David Cox and Erica James;
adapted by David Calcutt
  single: 0 19 918784 3
  pack of 6: 0 19 918785 1

**Stage 12**
**The Lie Detector**
by Susan Gates;
adapted by David Calcutt
  single: 0 19 918788 6
  pack of 6: 0 19 918789 4

**Blue Shoes**
by Angela Bull;
adapted by David Calcutt
  single: 0 19 918790 8
  pack of 6: 0 19 918791 6

**Stage 13**
**The Personality Potion**
by Alan MacDonald;
adapted by David Calcutt
  single: 0 19 918792 4
  pack of 6: 0 19 918793 2

**Spooky!**
by Michaela Morgan;
adapted by David Calcutt
  single: 0 19 918794 0
  pack of 6: 0 19 918795 9

**Stage 14**
**Petey**
by Paul Shipton;
adapted by David Calcutt
  single: 0 19 918796 7
  pack of 6: 0 19 918797 5

**Climbing in the Dark**
adapted from his own novel
by Nick Warburton
  single: 0 19 918798 3
  pack of 6: 0 19 918799 1